GOSCINNY AND UDERZO
PRESENT
An Asterix Adventure

ASTERIX
AND
CLEOPATRA

Written by RENÉ GOSCINNY *and Illustrated by* ALBERT UDERZO

Translated by Anthea Bell *and* Derek Hockridge

ORION

© 1965 GOSCINNY/UDERZO
Revised edition and English translation © 2004 HACHETTE

Original title: *Astérix et Cléopâtre*

Original edition © 1965 Dargaud Editeur

Exclusive Licensee: Orion Publishing Group
Translators: Anthea Bell and Derek Hockridge
Typography: Bryony Newhouse

The right of René Goscinny and Albert Uderzo to be identified as the authors of this work
has been asserted in accordance with the Copyright, Designs and Patents Act 1988.

First published in Great Britain in 1969 by Brockhampton Press Ltd

This revised edition first published in 2004 by
Orion Books Ltd
Orion House, 5 Upper St Martin's Lane
London WC2H 9EA

Printed in France by Partenaires

www.asterix.tm.fr

A CIP catalogue record for this book is available from the British Library

ISBN 0 752866109 (cased)
ISBN 0 752866117 (paperback)

GAULISH VILLAGE

COMPENDIUM

LAUDANUM

AQUARIUM

TOTORUM

ARMORICA

BELGICA

• LUTETIA

GAUL

(ROMAN CONQUEST)

50 BC

CELTICA

AQUITANIA

PROVINCIA

THE YEAR IS 50 BC. GAUL IS ENTIRELY OCCUPIED BY THE
ROMANS. WELL, NOT ENTIRELY ... ONE SMALL VILLAGE OF
INDOMITABLE GAULS STILL HOLDS OUT AGAINST THE INVADERS.
AND LIFE IS NOT EASY FOR THE ROMAN LEGIONARIES WHO
GARRISON THE FORTIFIED CAMPS OF TOTORUM, AQUARIUM,
LAUDANUM AND COMPENDIUM ...

ASTERIX, THE HERO OF THESE ADVENTURES. A SHREWD, CUNNING LITTLE WARRIOR, ALL PERILOUS MISSIONS ARE IMMEDIATELY ENTRUSTED TO HIM. ASTERIX GETS HIS SUPERHUMAN STRENGTH FROM THE MAGIC POTION BREWED BY THE DRUID GETAFIX . . .

OBELIX, ASTERIX'S INSEPARABLE FRIEND. A MENHIR DELIVERY MAN BY TRADE, ADDICTED TO WILD BOAR. OBELIX IS ALWAYS READY TO DROP EVERYTHING AND GO OFF ON A NEW ADVENTURE WITH ASTERIX – SO LONG AS THERE'S WILD BOAR TO EAT, AND PLENTY OF FIGHTING. HIS CONSTANT COMPANION IS DOGMATIX, THE ONLY KNOWN CANINE ECOLOGIST, WHO HOWLS WITH DESPAIR WHEN A TREE IS CUT DOWN.

GETAFIX, THE VENERABLE VILLAGE DRUID, GATHERS MISTLETOE AND BREWS MAGIC POTIONS. HIS SPECIALITY IS THE POTION WHICH GIVES THE DRINKER SUPERHUMAN STRENGTH. BUT GETAFIX ALSO HAS OTHER RECIPES UP HIS SLEEVE . . .

CACOFONIX, THE BARD. OPINION IS DIVIDED AS TO HIS MUSICAL GIFTS. CACOFONIX THINKS HE'S A GENIUS. EVERY-ONE ELSE THINKS HE'S UNSPEAKABLE. BUT SO LONG AS HE DOESN'T SPEAK, LET ALONE SING, EVERYBODY LIKES HIM . . .

FINALLY, VITALSTATISTIX, THE CHIEF OF THE TRIBE. MAJESTIC, BRAVE AND HOT-TEMPERED, THE OLD WARRIOR IS RESPECTED BY HIS MEN AND FEARED BY HIS ENEMIES. VITALSTATISTIX HIMSELF HAS ONLY ONE FEAR, HE IS AFRAID THE SKY MAY FALL ON HIS HEAD TOMORROW. BUT AS HE ALWAYS SAYS, TOMORROW NEVER COMES.

ALEXANDRIA, CAPITAL OF EGYPT. THE PALACE OF THE FABULOUS QUEEN CLEOPATRA, OF WHOM IT WAS SAID THAT IF HER NOSE HAD BEEN SHORTER IT WOULD HAVE CHANGED THE WHOLE COURSE OF HISTORY...

THAT'S AN INFAMOUS SUGGESTION, O CAESAR!

YOU HAVE TO FACE FACTS, O QUEEN! YOURS IS A DECADENT NATION, ONLY FIT TO LIVE IN SEMI-SLAVERY UNDER THE ROMANS.

MY PEOPLE BUILT THE PYRAMIDS! THE TOWER OF PHAROS! THE TEMPLES – THE OBELISKS!

THAT'S OLD HAT! ALL THEY CAN DO NOW IS WAIT FOR THE ANNUAL FLOODING OF THE NILE!

THAT WILL DO!

CRASH!

I, CLEOPATRA, WILL PROVE TO YOU, O CAESAR, THAT MY PEOPLE ARE AS BRILLIANT AS EVER! IN THREE MONTHS' TIME I'LL HAVE A MAGNIFICENT PALACE BUILT HERE FOR YOU IN ALEXANDRIA!

WELL, IF YOU CAN DO THAT, O QUEEN, I'LL ADMIT THAT THE EGYPTIANS ARE STILL A GREAT NATION...

...BUT I HAVE MY DOUBTS!

SHE'S A NICE GIRL, ONLY HER NOSE IS SO EASILY PUT OUT OF JOINT...

CRASH!

...PRETTY NOSE TOO!

5

SOON AFTER-WARDS...

N.B. FOR THE CONVENIENCE OF OUR READERS, WE GIVE A DUBBED VERSION OF THE ORIGINAL DIALOGUE...

EDIFIS, I HAVE SUMMONED YOU BECAUSE YOU ARE THE BEST ARCHITECT IN ALEXANDRIA ...WHICH ISN'T SAYING MUCH.

OH!*

* OWING TO THE FACT THAT DUBBING TECHNIQUES HAD NOT BEEN PERFECTED AT THIS PERIOD, THE MOVEMENT OF THE LIPS DOES NOT SYNCHRONIZE VERY WELL WITH THE WORDS.

DON'T ANSWER BACK! YOUR BUILDINGS ARE FLIMSY! YOU CAN HEAR EVERY WORD THE NEIGHBOURS SAY! THE CEILINGS FALL IN!

IT'S THESE MODERN MATERIALS... ACTUALLY, WHAT I REALLY WANT TO DO IS BUILD PYRAMIDS AND...

SILENCE! YOU HAVE JUST THREE MONTHS TO MAKE GOOD. YOU ARE TO BUILD JULIUS CAESAR A MAGNIFICENT PALACE HERE IN ALEXANDRIA.

DID YOU SAY **THREE MONTHS?**

IF YOU SUCCEED I WILL COVER YOU WITH GOLD! IF NOT, YOU'LL BE THROWN TO THE CROCODILES! YOU MAY GO!

THREE MONTHS! I'D NEED SUPERNATURAL POWERS TO DO THAT! I'D NEED SOMEONE WHO CAN WORK MAGIC...

GOT IT!
I KNOW THE VERY MAN! HE CAN WORK MAGIC!

CLAC!

AND FAR AWAY, IN A LITTLE VILLAGE IN GAUL...

VI.VI.VI*
AGAIN, IT'S LIKE MAGIC!

HA! HA! IT **IS** MAGIC!

THIS ROMAN GAME WILL NEVER CATCH ON...

* 3 SIXES

MY SHIP IS WAITING OFFSHORE.

JUST GIVE US TIME TO PACK AND SAY GOODBYE, AND WE'LL BE WITH YOU!

COME ALONG, DOGMATIX, WE'RE GOING ON A NICE SEA VOYAGE!

YOU'RE NEVER GOING TO TAKE HIM?

AND WHY NOT, MAY I ASK, MR ASTERIX?

BECAUSE HE'S TOO SMALL FOR SUCH A LONG JOURNEY, THAT'S WHY NOT, MR OBELIX!

WHAT'S MORE, THERE ARE CATS IN EGYPT! NO, NOT ANOTHER WORD! YOU GO AND PACK.

IT'S ALWAYS THE SAME! I'M JUST AN EXTRA! A MAKEWEIGHT! NO ONE EVER LISTENS TO ME!

SOON AFTERWARDS

YOU, MY FRIENDS, ARE TO REPRESENT THE SPIRIT OF GAUL ON THE BANKS OF THE NILE! SHOW YOURSELVES TRUE-BORN GAULS, BY TOUTATIS, AND MAY THE SKY NEVER FALL ON YOUR HEADS!

HEY!

GOODBYE, THEN, AND THANKS, CHIEF VITALSTATISTIX!

HEY!

EH?

NO, CACOFONIX, YOU ARE NOT, REPEAT NOT, GOING TO SING!!!

BOING! BOING! BOING!

BUT I WASN'T GOING TO SING! I ONLY WANTED TO TELL HIM HE WAS TREADING ON MY TOE!

SOON AFTERWARDS...

WOOF!

?

JUST ME BARKING! I CAN BARK, CAN'T I, EVEN IF I'M NOT ALLOWED TO TALK?

ALL RIGHT, YOU WIN, YOU PIGHEADED GREAT IDIOT! LET HIM OUT!

THERE'S MY SHIP, THE NASTIUPSET.

WE CAN CAST OFF NOW, SETHISBACKUP.

HONESTLY, ASTERIX, I SWEAR I DON'T KNOW HOW HE GOT INTO MY BAG!

NO, NO, OF COURSE NOT! HURRY UP OR WE'LL MISS THE TIDE.

AND WITH AN ICY WINTER WIND BEHIND THEM, OUR FRIENDS SET SAIL ON THEIR LONG VOYAGE TO EGYPT AND THE FABULOUS CLEOPATRA...

IN EGYPT WE SHALL HAVE TO CONTEND WITH LABOUR TROUBLES, THE TIME FACTOR, THE ROMANS, WHO WON'T WANT US TO WIN CLEOPATRA'S BET...

AND ABOVE ALL WITH ARTIFIS, A RIVAL ARCHITECT. HE'S ALWAYS GOT IT IN FOR ME. HE HAS A LOT OF TALENTS...

CLEVER, IS HE?

NO, RICH. HE HAS A LOT OF GOLD TALENTS – THAT'S THE MONEY WE USE IN EGYPT.

AND THEN THERE'S ALWAYS THE DANGER OF PIRATES ON THE WAY.

OH, WE'LL TAKE CARE OF THAT! RIGHT, OBELIX?

SURE ENOUGH, NOT FAR AWAY...

RIGHT, BOYS! WE'RE STEERING CLEAR OF ALL GAULS THIS TIME! AVOID ROMAN AND PHOENICIAN VESSELS TOO – THEY SOMETIMES USE THOSE. I'M PLAYING SAFE... I HAD TO LEAVE MY SON ERIX ON DEPOSIT TO BUY THIS SHIP!

NEXT INSTALMENT COMING UP, SIR! EGYPTIAN SHIP TO STARBOARD.

SPLENDID! WE'LL MAKE OUR FORTUNES! WE'LL DO IT YET! GET READY TO BOARD HER!

9

WHAT'S THE LOOKOUT SAYING?

HE SAYS THERE'S A PIRATE SHIP TO PORT.

HONEST? YOU'RE NOT JOKING?

IT'S THEM, ASTERIX, IT'S THEM! **YOOHOO! YOOHOO!** COMiNG!

IT ISN'T TRUE! IT **CAN'T** BE TRUE! IT'S THEM! GET OUT OF HERE, FAST! QUICK, SCUTTLE!

TOO LATE, CAP'N! THEY'RE SCUTTLING FASTER!

SCUTTLE THE SHIP, I MEAN! SAVES US A FEW KNOCKS, AND COMES TO THE SAME THING IN THE END.

SOON AFTERWARDS...

WELL, YOU SAID WE'D DO IT, AND HERE WE ARE, DONE! ALEA JACTA EST!

ONE MORE CLASSICAL REMARK FROM YOU AND I'LL MAKE YOU EAT YOUR WOODEN LEG!

OFFSIDE! FOUL! UNSPORTING!

AMAZING! THOSE PIRATES TOOK ONE LOOK AT YOU AND SANK THEIR OWN SHIP RATHER THAN FIGHT!

OH, WE'RE OLD FRIENDS... WE OFTEN GO SAILING TOGETHER.

ONE NIGHT, AFTER A LONG, PEACEFUL VOYAGE...

WHAT'S THAT LIGHT ON THE HORIZON, EDIFIS?

IT'S THE TOWER OF PHAROS, ASTERIX. ITS LIGHT GUIDES SHIPS INTO THE HARBOUR...

WE'LL REACH ALEXANDRIA TOMORROW.

A TOWER TO GUIDE SHIPS? THESE EGYPTIANS ARE CRAZY!

THIS, MY DEAR OBELIX, IS ONE OF THE SEVEN WONDERS OF THE WORLD!

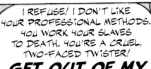

DURING THE LENTIL* BREAK THE LABOURERS HAVE AN UNEXPECTED VISITOR...

* A VERY POPULAR ANCIENT EGYPTIAN DISH

?! !?!

?! ?!?

? ?!

?

...WHOSE REMARKS ARE EVIDENTLY OF ABSORBING INTEREST.

TEEHEEHEE!

AND AT THE END OF THE LENTIL BREAK...

BOUHOU! OUHO

...THE LABOURERS MAKE IT PERFECTLY CLEAR...

...THAT THEY ARE NOT GOING BACK TO WORK.

MASTER! THE LABOURERS WON'T GO ON WITH THE JOB! I THINK SOMEONE'S BEEN STIRRING THEM UP AGAINST YOU!

?

ALL THESE WORRIES ARE POSITIVELY BLOOD-CURDLING! BY THE TIME THE CROCODILES GET ME I'LL BE QUITE UNEATABLE!

ALL THE BETTER! ARE YOU SO KEEN TO MAKE THEM A GOOD MEAL?

BUT THOSE ARE SACRED CROCODILES! YOU CAN'T JUST FEED THEM ANY OLD THING!

THESE EGYPTIANS ARE CRAZY!

TAP! TAP! TAP!

THESE AMAZING FOREIGN WIZARDS WILL END UP HELPING EDIFIS TO WIN! I MUST DO SOMETHING!

KRUKHUT!

WHAT IS IT, ARTIFIS, MY MASTER?

I KNOW EDIFIS IS EXPECTING A CONSIGNMENT OF STONE TO COME DOWN THE NILE FROM THE COUNTRY. THAT STONE MUST NEVER REACH THE BUILDING SITE... HERE'S GOLD TO SETTLE THE BUSINESS!

KRUKHUT MEETS THE FLEET BRINGING STONE FOR THE PALACE, AND HIS GOLD QUICKLY OVERCOMES THE CAPTAIN'S SCRUPLES...

* UNLOAD THOSE STONES!

* NOT ON THE BANK! THE OTHER SIDE!

BONK!

THE LABOURERS, NATIVES OF THE RURAL DISTRICTS OF EGYPT, OBEY WITHOUT QUESTION.

SPLOSH!

SPLASH!

* BAIN'T NO USE ARGUFYING WITH HE!

* OI RECKON GAFFER BE CRAZY!

SOON AFTERWARDS

WE SHALL BE JOINING THE NILE AND THEN FOLLOWING THE RIVER SOUTH.

MEANWHILE, IN THE HOUSE OF THE INFAMOUS ARTIFIS...

I'VE LEARNT THAT THOSE MIRACLE-WORKING FOREIGNERS HAVE GONE OFF TO GET MORE STONE. KRUKHUT, THEY MUST NOT RETURN! THIS IS WHAT YOU HAVE TO DO...

THE FLEET GLIDES SLOWLY DOWN THE MAJESTIC AND SACRED RIVER NILE...

THIS IS SLOW!

VERY SLOW!

TOO SLOW!

ALL MOVE TO THE BANK! FASTEN THE BOATS FIRMLY TOGETHER WITH ROPES!

A BIT OF EXERCISE AT LAST!

?

BY TOUTATIS, THAT BOY NEVER CEASES TO SURPRISE ME, EVEN THOUGH I DO KNOW HE FELL INTO A CAULDRON FULL OF MAGIC POTION WHEN HE WAS A BABY!

AT NIGHTFALL THEY CAMP ON THE RIVER BANK...

LENTILS AGAIN! NOT A SINGLE SLICE OF BOAR! AND THEN THEY'LL WONDER WHY I'VE COME OVER WEAK!

TOMORROW WE'LL VISIT THE SPHINX AND THE PYRAMIDS. IT'S NOT FAR AWAY, AND THEY'RE WORTH SEEING!

BUT UNDER COVER OF DARKNESS A CUNNING SPY IS WATCHING AND WAITING.

TEE HEE HEE!

16

SO NOW YOU KNOW WHY THE SPHINX HAS NO NOSE. WHICH IS A PITY, FOR THE SPHINX'S NOSE, LOST TO THIS DAY, WAS A VERY FINE SPECIMEN OF A NOSE, IF NOT SO BEAUTIFUL AS CLEOPATRA'S, WHICH, AS WE BELIEVE WE MENTIONED BEFORE, WAS A VERY PRETTY NOSE INDEED.

INSIDE THE PYRAMID...

MY POWERS ARE NOT STRONG ENOUGH TO GET US OUT OF HERE... I AM VERY MUCH AFRAID THIS MAY BE THE END OF OUR ADVENTURES, BY BELENOS!

I'M ONLY SORRY FOR EDIFIS... WITHOUT OUR HELP HE'LL END UP INSIDE A CROCODILE.

WELL, I'M SORRY FOR MY POOR LITTLE DOGMATIX... AREN'T I, DOGMATIX?

DOGMATIX?!

YES, DOGMATIX! WHAT ABOUT IT? YOU'RE NOT GOING TO BE CROSS WITH ME FOR BRINGING HIM? ANYWAY, I DIDN'T BRING HIM, HE CAME ALL BY HIMSELF!

EXACTLY! HE'S FOUND US THANKS TO HIS NOSE... IN WHICH CASE HE CAN FIND HIS WAY BACK AGAIN AND SHOW US THE WAY OUT!

BY BELENOS, YOU'RE RIGHT!

DOGMATIX, IF YOU HELP US OUT OF HERE YOU'LL GET A VERY BIG BONE OUTSIDE!

YOU'LL GET TWO BIG BONES!

HEAPS OF BIG BONES!

OBELIX, I APOLOGIZE! YOU WERE QUITE RIGHT TO BRING YOUR DOGGIE!

SOMETIMES I FEEL HE UNDERSTANDS EVERYTHING I SAY!

25

1 THE FOREIGNERS HAVE DISAPPEARED, THERE'S NO NEED FOR YOU TO GO ON WITH YOUR JOURNEY.
2 I GOT IT FIRST TIME.

IT'S MAGIC! YOU'RE WIZARDS! ONLY A SUPERMAN COULD EVER FIND HIS WAY OUT OF...

WHAM!

THE BOATS SET OFF AGAIN AND SAIL PEACEFULLY ON UP THE NILE...

SCRUNCH! SCRUNCH! SCRUNCH!

...STOPPING OFF TO SEE THE SIGHTS AT INTERESTING SPOTS SUCH AS LUXOR...

NO, NO, AND FOR THE THIRD TIME NO, OBELIX! THAT THING IN THE MIDDLE OF THE VILLAGE? IT WOULD JUST LOOK SILLY.

WE SHALL NEVER BE IN CONCORD OVER THIS!

MEANWHILE, BACK AT ALEXANDRIA...

O ARTIFIS, MY MASTER... THEY'RE WIZARDS! THEY HAVE SUPERHUMAN POWERS!

!?

THEY'VE MANAGED TO GET OUT OF THE LABYRINTH OF THE GREAT PYRAMID!

FANTASTIC! THEY'RE JUST FANTASTIC!

ALL THE MORE REASON TO FIND SOME WAY OF STOPPING THEM! EDIFIS MUST NOT BUILD THAT PALACE, KRUKHUT!

AFTER A VOYAGE OF MANY STADIA*

MY FRIENDS! BACK AT LAST!

AND WE'VE BROUGHT YOU ENOUGH STONE TO FINISH THE PALACE!

* STADIUM: ROMAN MEASURE OF ABOUT 184 METRES. AS THERE ARE 30·48 CENTIMETRES IN A FOOT, AND 12 FEET IN AN ALEXANDRINE, IT IS EASY TO WORK OUT THAT THERE ARE ABOUT 50½ ALEXANDRINES IN ONE STADIUM.

THE LABOURERS, WELL DOSED WITH MAGIC POTION, WORK SWIFTLY.

IF I WASN'T HERE TO CORRECT THESE PLANS...

I'VE JUST HEARD THAT CLEOPATRA'S COMING TO VISIT THE BUILDING SITE!

SURE ENOUGH...

OH, DON'T STOP! I'M JUST PAYING A QUIET VISIT, INCOGNITO. DO GO ON!

THERE'S NO DENYING IT, SHE DOES HAVE A PRETTY NOSE!

A VERY PRETTY NOSE!

DID YOU SEE HER NOSE, DOGMATIX?

MEANWHILE, IN ARTIFIS'S HOUSE...

AN IDEA! I NEED AN IDEA!

HELP ME! **AND FOR THE LAST TIME GO AND SHAVE YOUR HEAD!**

I CAN'T, MASTER. I MADE A VOW...

I'VE GOT IT! IT'S A PIECE OF CAKE!

SLAP!

23

27

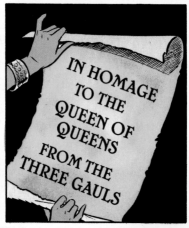

DRINK THIS, TASTER. YOU'LL FEEL BETTER!

OH, SO THUMPING THEM IS ALL RIGHT BUT EATING ALMONDS ISN'T?

THERE'S A TIME FOR THUMPING PEOPLE AND A TIME FOR EATING ALMONDS! THAT'S GOOD MANNERS!

* GLUG, GLUG, GLUG

I FEEL BETTER... MUCH BETTER...

WHY, I FEEL FINE! I'M HUNGRY!

THAT CAKE HAD NOTHING TO DO WITH YOUR TASTER'S ILLNESS, O QUEEN. HE JUST HAS A DELICATE STOMACH FROM EATING TOO MUCH RICH FOOD!

I HAVE TREATED YOU UNJUSTLY, O GAULS! YOU SHALL GO FREE! AS FOR THIS TASTER, WHOSE STOMACH HAS CAUSED ME, THE QUEEN OF QUEENS, TO MAKE A MISTAKE, I DISMISS HIM!

THERE WAS ENOUGH POISON IN THAT CAKE FOR A WHOLE COHORT OF LEGIONARIES. IT'S A GOOD THING WE DRANK MY ANTIDOTE...

I SAY, THANK YOU VERY MUCH! I FOUND THE JOB OF TASTER VERY DISTASTEFUL... IT WAS POISONING MY LIFE.

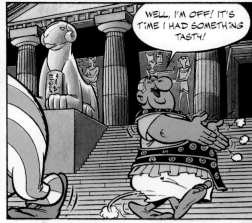

WELL, I'M OFF! IT'S TIME I HAD SOMETHING TASTY!

LET'S GET BACK TO THE BUILDING SITE. WE MUST FIND OUT WHO WAS RESPONSIBLE FOR THIS OUTRAGE!

ASTERIX, WHAT IS AN ANTIDOTE?

AND AT THE BUILDING SITE...

DOGMATIX! YOU NEARLY KNOCKED ME OVER!

THANK RA YOU'RE BACK! MY MASTER EDIFIS DISAPPEARED IMMEDIATELY AFTER YOU WERE ARRESTED!

!!!

OBELIX, WE'RE GOING TO SEE ARTIFIS. I'M SURE HE'LL KNOW WHERE EDIFIS IS!

SOON AFTERWARDS

IT'S THAT WAY, ACCORDING TO THE DIRECTIONS EXLIBRIS GAVE ME.

SCHOOL

OPEN UP, BY BELENOS, IF YOU VALUE YOUR DOOR!

WHAT'S ALL THIS NOISE, BY...

THE GAU... THE GAUGAU...

YES, THE GAULS, AND WE WANT TO SEE YOUR MASTER ARTIFIS.

I... I'LL GO AND SEE IF HE'S IN...

GOOD IDEA! WE'LL COME WITH YOU!

BOSS! SOMEONE TO SEE YOU...

?!

Daily Nile

PTARZAN

PNUTS

YOU? DIDN'T CLEOPATRA THROW YOU TO THE CROCODI...

THAT'S A CONFESSION!

SO IT WAS YOU WHO SENT CLEOPATRA THE POISONED CAKE?

CAKE? WHAT CAKE? NO, NO, NO! IT'S ALL A MISTAKE. JUST A MISTAKE! OH RA!

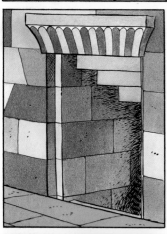

ARE YOU ALL RIGHT, EDIFIS?

NOT BAD... A LITTLE DIZZY!

POOR OLD EDIFIS, IT MUST BE ON ACCOUNT OF HIS SUFFERINGS!

I GIVE IN! I HOPED TO STOP YOU FINISHING THE PALACE. NO HARD FEELINGS?

NO HARD FEELINGS, AND TO PROVE IT WE'LL TAKE YOU TWO ALONG WITH US. WE'VE GOT A JOB FOR YOU.

SOON AFTERWARDS, AT THE BUILDING SITE...

THIS IS WHAT COMES OF ALL THOSE WICKED THINGS YOU MADE ME DO, BOSS!

SHUT UP AND PULL, WILL YOU!

THE BUILDING'S COMING ALONG NICELY, EDIFIS.

THANKS TO YOU THREE, GETAFIX!

31A

MEANWHILE, IN CLEOPATRA'S PALACE...

AVE, CLEOPATRA. WELL, HOW'S THE PALACE GOING? TIME WILL SOON BE UP.

AVE, CAESAR. OH, IT'S GETTING ON NICELY, THANKS, JULIUS! WE'LL SOON BE ABLE TO HAVE A LITTLE PALACE WARMING.

AVE, CAESAR!

AVE! LEGIONARY, GO AND FIND MINTJULEP MY EGYPTIAN SPY.

AVE, CAESAR!

AVE, AVE, MINTJULEP. I LOOK LIKE LOSING FACE WITH CLEOPATRA...

I WAS TOLD THAT EDIFIS THE ARCHITECT WAS A NITWIT, BUT NOW IT SEEMS THE PALACE WILL BE READY IN TIME. GO TO THE BUILDING SITE AND SEE WHAT'S GOING ON, BY JUPITER!

31W

* ANCIENT GAULISH WAR-SONG

WHAM!

BOING!

MY PALACE!

WE'LL HAVE TO LET CLEOPATRA KNOW! SHE MUST HAVE ENOUGH INFLUENCE OVER CAESAR TO GET THIS ATTACK STOPPED.

GOOD IDEA! EXLIBRIS! WRITE THE QUEEN A MESSAGE.

NOW THEN... NO SPELLING MISTAKES...

👁 BEFORE 🦅 EXCEPT AFTER 〰

TCHONK!

DOGMATIX WILL CARRY THE MESSAGE TO CLEOPATRA!

DOGMATIX?!

BUT DOGMATIX IS ONLY A PUPPY!

MAYBE, BUT HE'S VERY INTELLIGENT!

HERE'S THE MESSAGE!

YOU'LL SEE!

SEEK, DOGMATIX! CLEOPATRA! SEEK!

I TOLD YOU HE WAS TOO YOUNG TO UNDERSTAND!

TOO YOUNG! A LITTLE DOG WHO CAN BEG SO NICELY, AND SO ON...

THERE, THERE, OBELIX, DON'T BE CROSS! I WAS ONLY TEASING. I'LL SHOW HIM THE RIGHT WAY MYSELF!

FANCY SAYING MY DOG'S NO GOOD!

QUICK, GETAFIX, WHILE OBELIX ISN'T LOOKING! GIVE ME A GOOD SWIG OF MAGIC POTION!

RHUBARBRHUBARBRHU... BARBRHUB ARBRHUBARBRHU...

SOON AFTERWARDS

OFF WE GO, DOGMATIX!

41

WATCH OUT! ONE OF THE BESIEGED MEN IS TRYING TO BREAK OUT!!

WHOOSH!

READY?

READY!

KERPLONK!

?

BOING!

HE WENT THE SAME WAY HE CAME...

JUST PASSING THROUGH...

SOON AFTERWARDS, IN CLEOPATRA'S PALACE...

YOU WANTED TO SEE ME, O GAUL?

YES, O CLEOPATRA. MY LITTLE DOG HAS A MESSAGE FOR YOU.

ISN'T HE SWEET! BRING A BONE FOR THIS LITTLE DOG!

THIS WILL NEVER DO! JULIUS CAESAR ISN'T PLAYING FAIR, BY ISIS! YOU MAY GO, GAUL! BY AMMON AND BY HELIOS, I'LL SEE TO THIS!

SCRUNCH! SCRUNCH! SCRUNCH!

GRRRRRR

KEEP STILL, DOGMATIX! WAIT TILL THE QUEEN'S NEW TASTER HAS TASTED YOUR BONE.

WATCH OUT! ONE OF THE BESIEGED MEN IS TRYING TO BREAK IN AGAIN!

WHOOSH!

HERE YOU ARE, OBELIX! DOGMATIX HAS JUST GOT BACK! HE DID HIS JOB PERFECTLY!

THERE YOU ARE! YOU SEE?

LET'S HOPE THE QUEEN ACTS QUICKLY. THE ROMAN MISSILES ARE DESTROYING THE PALACE!

SURE ENOUGH, IN THE CAMP OF THE BESIEGING ARMY...

THERE YOU ARE, CAESAR! EVEN IF WE DON'T CAPTURE THEM THE PALACE WILL BE DESTROYED JUST THE SAME!

EXCELLENT, OPERACHORUS, EXCELLENT!

AVE, CAESAR... ER... SOMEONE WANTS TO SPEAK TO YOU...

WHO IS IT?

ZING!
BOOM!

TAPTAPTAP!
TAPTAPTAP!

TANTANTARA!!!

?!?

ER... QUEEN...
MY DEAR QUEEN...

THAT'S ENOUGH OF THAT! WHEN I HEARD WHAT WAS HAPPENING I HURRIED OUT OF THE PALACE AT ONCE! I DIDN'T EVEN STOP TO CHANGE!

OOPS!

WHEN YOU MAKE A BET YOU MUST PLAY FAIR AND I HAD A RIGHT TO CALL IN THE GAULS AND I'LL PROVE TO YOU THAT EGYPTIANS CAN BUILD BEAUTIFUL PALACES...

...AND I ABSOLUTELY INSIST THAT THE ROMANS LEAVE THE BUILDERS IN PEACE AND REPAIR ALL THE DAMAGE THEY'VE DONE BEFORE LEAVING AND IT'S A CRYING SHAME...

...AND...

ALL RIGHT! ALL RIGHT! DON'T GO ON! I'M SORRY AND I'LL DO WHAT YOU WANT...

ZING!
BOOM!
TANTANTARA!

PHEW!

WELL... ER... NOW WHAT DO WE DO?

RAISE THE SIEGE AND REPAIR THE DAMAGE YOU'VE DONE, IDIOT!

AVE!

AFTER ALL, I WOULDN'T WANT CLEOPATRA TO TURN HER NOSE UP AT ME!

A VERY PRETTY NOSE, IN CASE WE DIDN'T MENTION IT BEFORE...

LOOK! THE ROMANS ARE RAISING THE SIEGE, BY BELENOS!

VICTORY, BY TOUTATIS!

AND ALL THANKS TO WHO?

* A RARE OCCURRENCE IN THE BUILDING TRADE AT THAT TIME.

NEXT DAY...

NOT A BAD PALACE, IS IT?

HERE THEY ARE!

WHERE?

FOR YOU TO CUT THE RIBBON, O CAESAR!

O LOVELIEST OF QUEENS, YOURS IS THE HONOUR OF CUTTING THE RIBBON WHICH PROVES THAT I HAVE LOST MY BET, BY JUPITER! I YIELD WITH A GOOD GRACE BEFORE SO MUCH GRACE.

THE CROWD ACCLAIM THEIR QUEEN, INVOKING THE SUN-GOD OF EGYPT...

RA! RA! RA! RA! R

NOW WHO KNOWS BEST?

THAT'S A PRETTY KNOWS!

AT A BANQUET FOR 14,000 GUESTS (IT HAD BEEN PLANNED TO INVITE 13,000, BUT EGYPTIANS ARE SUPERSTITIOUS)...

YOU'VE SAVED MY LIFE AND TAUGHT ME MY JOB... MY GOLD IS YOURS!

NO, NO, IT WAS A PLEASURE. WHAT ARE YOU PLANNING NOW?

I'M FRIENDS WITH ARTIFIS AGAIN...

...TOGETHER WE'LL BUILD THE FINEST PYRAMIDS WITH THE SHARPEST POINTS IN EGYPT!

46

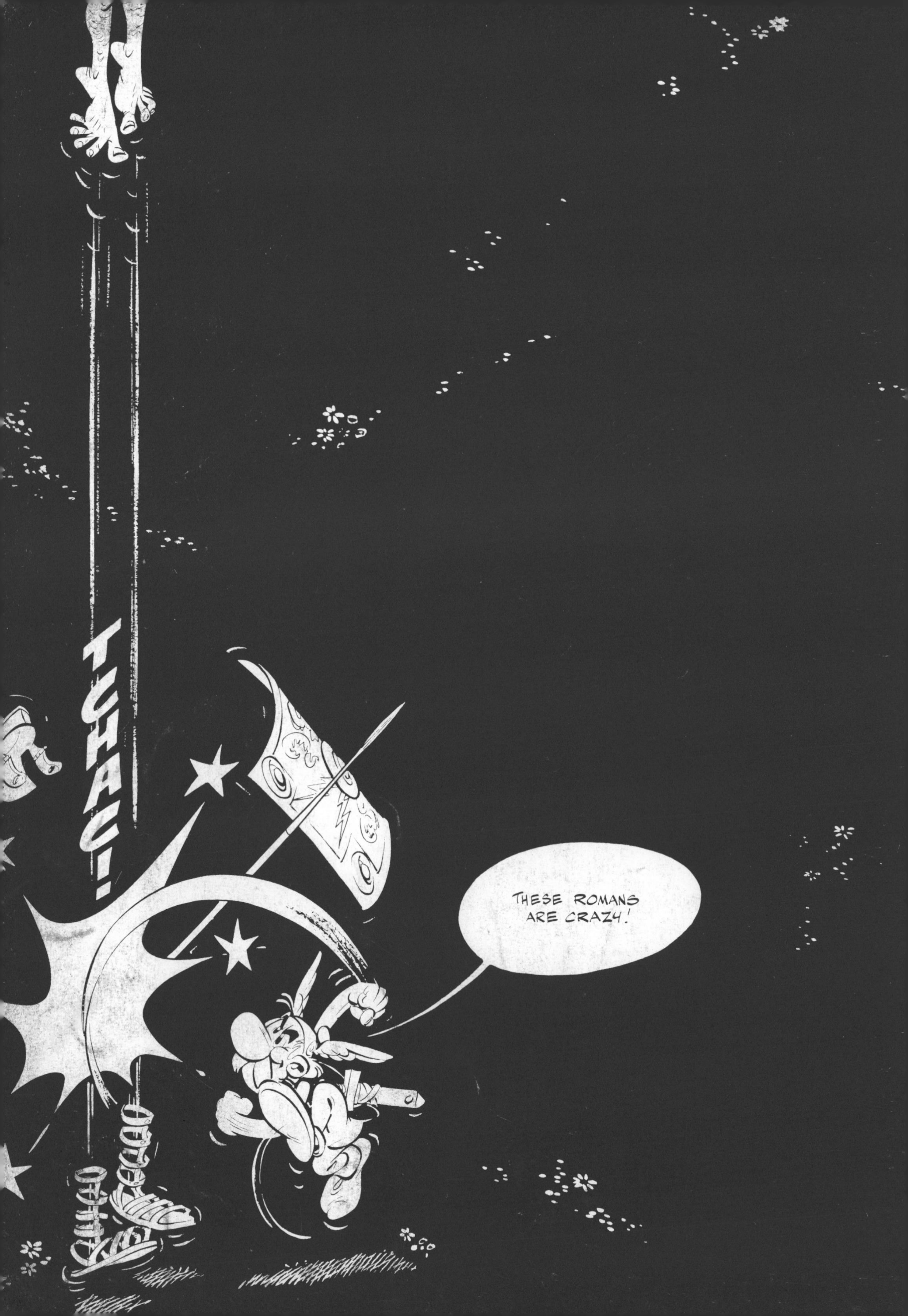
THWACK!
THESE ROMANS ARE CRAZY!